P. J. Redouté.

CHOIX

DES

PLUS BELLES FLEURS

PRISES DANS DIFFÉRENTES FAMILLES DU RÈGNE VÉGÉTAL

ET DE QUELQUES BRANCHES DES PLUS BEAUX FRUITS

GROUPÉES QUELQUEFOIS, ET SOUVENT ANIMÉES PAR DES INSECTES ET DES PAPILLONS

GRAVÉES, IMPRIMÉES EN COULEUR ET RETOUCHÉES AU PINCEAU AVEC UN SOIN QUI DOIT RÉPONDRE DE LEUR PERFECTION

PAR P. J. REDOUTÉ

PEINTRE ET PROFESSEUR D'ICONOGRAPHIE AU MUSÉE D'HISTOIRE NATURELLE, DESSINATEUR EN TITRE DE LA CLASSE DE PHYSIQUE
ET DE MATHÉMATIQUES DE L'INSTITUT, ETC., ETC.

PARIS

A LA LIBRAIRIE ENCYCLOPÉDIQUE DE RORET, RUE HAUTEFEUILLE, 42

THE
MOST BEAUTIFUL
FLOWERS

by Pierre Joseph Redouté

144 Engraved Color Plates

in Facsimile

Published by
WELLFLEET PRESS
110 Enterprise Avenue
Secaucus, New Jersey 07094

Reproduced with permission for North America
by William S. Konecky Associates, Inc.

All rights reserved.

ISBN: 1-55521-254-9

Printed and bound in Spain.

Preface

What is astonishing about the career of Pierre Joseph Redouté is the juxtaposition of a long line of Royal patronage with the equally enthusiastic welcome he enjoyed among the foremost French naturalists of the turbulent period in which he lived.

Called "the Raphael of Flowers" by early nineteenth century writers (who were nominating Mozart "the Raphael of music,") Pierre Joseph Redouté (1759–1840) was court painter and preceptor in four regimes, while being admired and sought after by a dozen of the leading naturalists and botanists of the time.

The most illustrious in a family of French artists, Redouté's grandfather (Jean-Jacques, 1687–1752) and father (Charles-Joseph, 1715–1776) were painters of portraits and landscapes, while two of his brothers also were painters in Paris (Antoine-Ferdinand, 1756–1809, and Henri-Joseph, 1766–1852—the first primarily as a decorator, and the other as a naturalist, member of the Egyptian Institute and associate at the Museum of Natural History, where Pierre Joseph Redouté was very active as well).

Living in Paris from 1782 on, in order Pierre Joseph was court painter for Princess Adelaide (1732–1808), Queen Marie Antionette (1755–1793), Empress Joséphine (1763–1814), Empress Marie-Louise (1791–1847), and finally Louis Philippe's Queen, Marie-Amélie (1782–1866). In France he was decorated with the Legion of Honor, and named Professor of Iconography; and recognition from the country of his birth, Belgium, came when he was awarded the Order of Leopold. Meanwhile, he counted among his friends and collaborators the foremost natural scientists of the generation of Jean-Baptiste Lamarck (1744–1829).

During the reign of Napoleon Redouté received a princely salary of 18,000 francs a year, and the French Emperor personally purchased a number of copies of Redouté's *Lilacs,* which he presented to various rulers of his time, while Napoleon's Minister of the Interior, Jean-Antonine Chaptal (1756–1832), subscribed to 80 copies of the book for distribution to a number of European artists. However, around 1800 the high cost of color printing made Redouté's acclaimed work unaffordable to even the upper bourgeoisie, and despite the undoubted artistic quality (many of the plates were touched by Redouté's own brush), and despite the meticulous accuracy of his work, each new production brought new debts to the artist. It was only in 1824 that Redouté was able to see the first of three editions of his *Roses*, printed by the publisher Panckoucke—an occasion which led to the further compliment "Rembrandt of Roses."

As the pinnacle of his craft Redouté created his *Most Beautiful Flowers*, on which he had worked intensively for six arduous years—the last of 36 series appeared in 1833. In this work he applied every technique and skill he had developed—depicting flowers, fruits as they were in nature, forming a truthful image in color, engraved, and even touched up personally—with a care their pristine perfection demanded. All the experience he had amassed in more than 6,000 watercolors for his Museum of Natural History, the illustrations for a *History of Juicy Plants, Lilacs,* the illustrations for Jean-Jacques Rousseau's *Botanical Letters, Roses*—all of his genial ability was demonstrated in this masterful volume. Redouté hoped that at last he would achieve financial success, and be able to pay his long overdue taxes, and back rent and other bills. However, neither this work, nor his later *Collection of Beautiful Small Flowers*, nor *The Seasons* could ease his financial difficulties, and on June 19, 1840, while painting a white lily, this master of flowers died in Paris at the age of 80.

Redouté's *Most Beautiful Flowers and Fruits* is not only accurate in color, but in form—he deserved his title of Dessinateur en Titre in the Department of Physics and Mathematics at the Institut de France. He made it possible for an entire generation of flower and botanical painters to flourish.

Original receipted bill (signed Redouté) October 27, 1820 concerning the delivery of numbers 1 – 18 of his *Histoire des Roses*.

VII.

Pierre Joseph Redouté, flower painter, engraver and lithographer, born July 10, 1759 (1758) in Saint-Hubert, near Liège, Belgium, died June 19, 1840, in Paris.

Famed for his precise technique, multi-colored printed and sometimes hand-colored representations of lilacs and roses

Bibliography

Geraniologia
Text by Charles Louis L'Héritier (1787–88), with black and white illustrations by Redouté and the Englishman James Sowerby.

Sertum Anglicum
Text by Charles Louis L'Héritier (1788), illustrations with the collaboration of Redouté.

Flora Atantica
Text by René L. Desfontaines, Volume II (1799), illustrations with the collaboration of Redouté.

Plantes Grasses (Short title of Plantarum succulentarum historia, or histoire naturelle des plantes grasses)
Text by Augustin Pagramus de Candolle (Decandolle), with illustrations by Redouté (1801–1803), in preparation since 1798).

Les Liliacées (1802–16)
Illustrations by Redouté, who was also the publisher.

Lettres élémentaires sur la botanique
Text by Jean Jacques Rousseau, Folio edition with Illustrations by Redouté (1805, 1821).

Les Roses I–III, 1817–1824;
second edition, 1824–26; third edition, 1828–30 ("small" Octavo edition). *Choix des plus belles fleurs prises dans difféentes familles du règne végétal et de quelques branches des plus beaux fruits, groupées quelques fois, et souvent animées par des insectes et des papillons.*
144 copper engravings printed in color by Panckoucke, Paris (1827–1833).
Later reprint with the title "Choix des plus belles fleurs et des plus beaux fruits."
Plates partially enhanced with hand-coloring.

Collection de jolies petites fleurs (choisies parmi les plus gracieuses productions de ce genre . . .) 1835-1836.

A Catalogue of Redouteana, Hunt Botanic Library, Pittsburg, Pennsylvania, 1963.

INDEX OF FRENCH NAMES

INDEX OF LATIN NAMES

PLATES

Numbers 25, 67, 135 were omitted by Redouté.
In place of them he inserted other plates:
59a, 89a, 114a (59 bis, 89 bis, 114 bis).

THE
MOST BEAUTIFUL
FLOWERS

Abricot-Pêche.

P. J. Redouté. _ I .   *Imprimerie de RORET, Rue Hautefeuille, 12 .*   Langlois.

Alstrœmeria Pelegrina.

P. J. Redouté _ 2.

Langlois.

Amaryllis equestre.

Amaryllis brésilienne   *Amaryllis bresiliensis.*

P. J. Redouté _ 4.   Victor

Amaryllis.

Lis St Jacques

P. J. Redouté. _ 5 .

Victor

Anémone étoilée.   *Anemone stellata.*

P. J. Redouté. __ 6.   *Victor.*

Anémone simple.　　　　　*Anemone simplex.*

P. J. Redouté ___ 7 .　　　　　Langlois.

Astelma eximium Gnaphale superbe

P. J. Redouté. — 8.   Chapuy.

Aster de Chine.

Aster Chinensis.

Bénoite écarlate.   *Geum coccineum.*

P. J. Redouté. _ 10 .

Chapuy.

Bignonia Capensis.

P. J. Redouté. _ 11.

Langlois.

Calville blanc.

Bouquet de Camélias Narcisses et Pensées.

P. J Redouté. *13.*

Victor

Camelia blanc.   *Camelia Japonica.*

P. J. Redouté. — 14.   Bessin.

Camélia (var.) *fleurs blanches.*　　　　　*Camelia Japonica.*

P. J. Redouté. — 15.　　　　　　　　　　　　　Langlois.

Camelia panaché.

Camelia Japonica.

P.J. Redouté _ 16.

Langlois.

Camelia a fleurs d'Anémone.   *Camelia Anemonefolia.*

P.J. Redouté. __ 17   Langlois.

Campanule Clochette.

P. J. Redouté. — 18.   Victor.

Campanule dentelée.   *Campanula.*

B J. Redouté. _ 19.   Langlois.

Cerisier Royal.

Cerasus domestica.

P. J. Redouté. _ 20.

Langlois.

Chevrefeuille.

Lonicera.

P. J. Redouté _ 21.

Victor.

Chrysanthème carené.   *Chrysanthemum carinatum.*

P. J. Redouté. _ 22.   Bessin

Clematis Viticella.

P. J. Redouté _ 23 .   Langlois

Corcopsis élégant.　　　　　*Corcopsis elegans.*

P. J. Redouté. — 24 .　　　　　Langlois.

Crocus sativus.　　　　　　　　*Safran cultivé.*

P. J. Redouté. _ 26 .　　　　　　　　Langlois.

Cyclamen.

P. J. Redouté. _ 27

Langlois.

Cyrtanthe oblique.

P. J. Redouté. — 28.

Cyrtanthus obliquus.

Bessin

Dalhia simple.　　　　　　　*Dalhia simplex.*

P. J. Redouté. — 29.　　　　　　　Bessin.

Dalhia double

Datura a fruit lisse.   *Datura Lavis.*

P. J. Redouté. _31.   Victor.

Dentelaire bleu de ciel.   *Plumbago cærulea.*

P. J. Redouté._ 32.   Bessin.

La Dillenne. *Dillenia scandens.*

P. J. Redouté. __ 33 . Langlois.

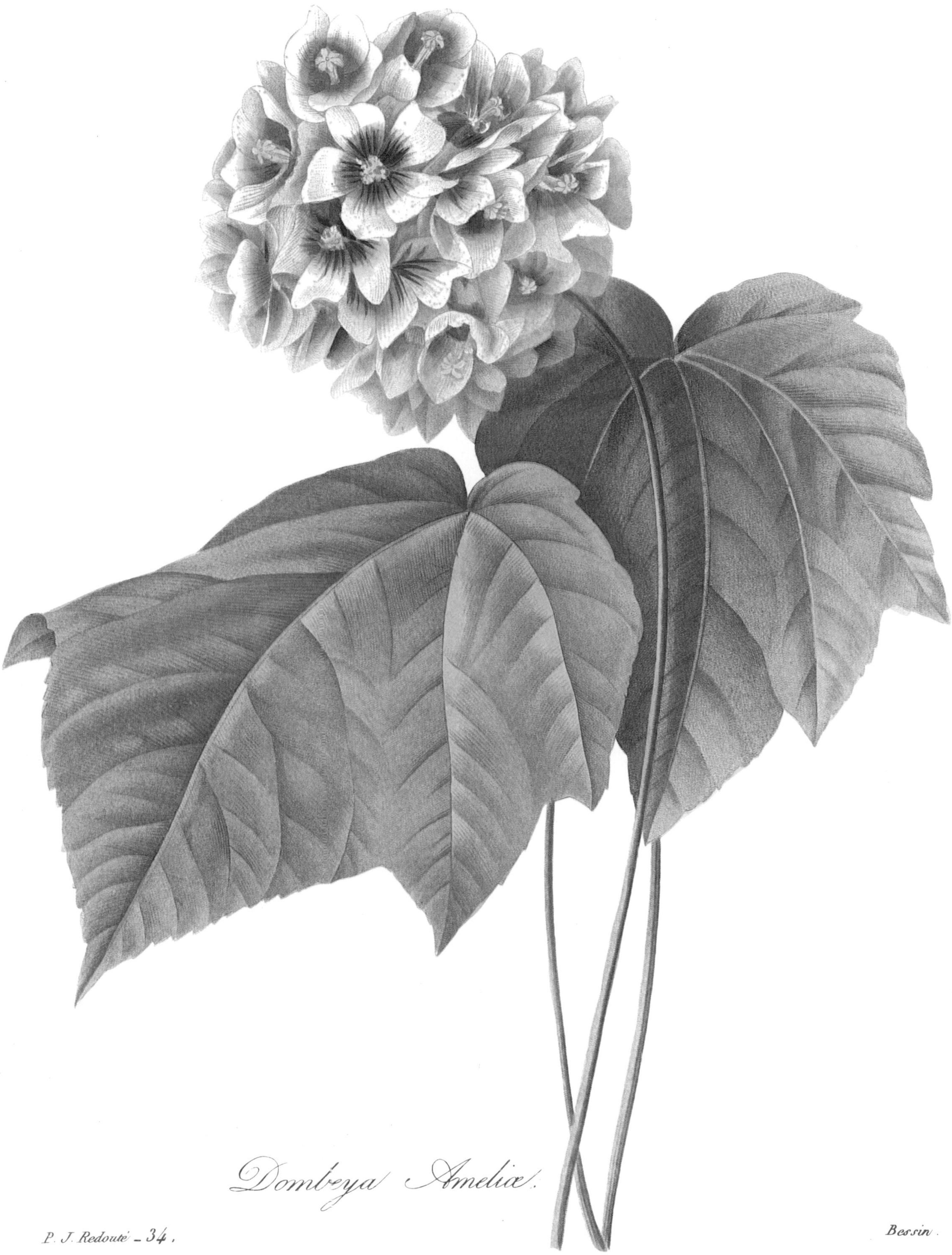

Dombeya Ameliæ.

P. J. Redouté – 34.

Bessin.

Ellébore.

P. J. Redouté. — 35.

Enkianthus Quinqueflorus

P. J. Redouté — 36 .

Bessin

Erica.

Bruyère.

P. J. Redouté. — 37.

Langlois.

Figue violette   *Ficus violacea*

P. J. Redouté. _ 38.   Bessin.

Fraisier à Bouquets.

Fragaria.

P. J. Redouté — 39.

Chapuis

Framboisier. *Rubus.*

P. J. Redouté. _ 40.

Langlois.

Fritillaire Impériale.

P. J. Redouté. _ 41.

Fritillaire Impériale Var. jaune.

P. J. Redouté. 42.

Victor.

Fuchsia écarlate.   *Fuchsia coccinea.*

P. J. Redouté. _ 43.

Galardia

Gentiane sans tige

Gentiana acaulis.

P. J. Redouté . . 45.

Langlois.

Geranium.

Varieté.

P. J. Redouté – 46.

Bessin.

Giroflée jaune.

Cheiranthus flavus.

Glayeul en pointe.

P. J. Redouté _ 48.

Gladiolus cuspidatus.

Langlois

Glayeul couleur de Laque.

Gladiolus Laccatus.

P. J. Redouté. _ 49.

Chapuy.

Grenade.   *Grenadier punica.*

P. J. Redouté. __50.   Victor.

Groseiller rouge.　　　　　　　　　　*Ribes rubrum.*

P. J. Redouté. _ 51.　　　　　　　　　　Langlois.

Heliotropium Corymbosum.

P. J. Redouté. __ 52

Langlois.

Hemerocallis Cærulea.

Althæa Frutex.

Hibiscus Syriacus.

P. J. Redouté. _ 54.

Bessin.

Mauve.   *Hibiscus trionum.*

P. J. Redouté. __ 55   Langlois

Hortensia.

Ipomæa Quamoclit.

P. J. Redouté. — 57.

Iris frangée.　　　　　　　　　　*Iris fimbriata.*

Iris pâle. *Iris pallida.*

P. J. Redouté. _59.   Victor.

Iris Xiphium. Variété.

P. J. Redouté. __ 59 bis   Langlois.

Iris Xiphium.   *Iris Xiphium.*

P. J. Redouté. _ 60.   Langlois.

1. Ixia a fleurs de Phlox.   *2. Niveole d'été.*

P. J. Redouté. _ 61.   Langlois.

Ixia a fleurs vertes.   *Ixia viridiflora.*

P. J. Redouté. _ 62.   Bessin.

Ixia tricolor.

Ixia tricolore.

P. J. Redouté. 63.

Victor.

Jacinthe d'orient variété rose.　　　　　　*Hyacinthus orientalis.*

P. J. Redouté. _ 64.　　　　　　　　　　Bessin.

Jacinthe d'Orient.

P. J. Redouté. _ 65.

Hyacinthus Orientalis.

Chapuy.

Jacinthe d'Orient Variété bleue.

Jasmin d'Espagne.

Jasminum grandiflorum.

P. J. Redouté. — 68.

Langlois.

Gesse a larges feuilles.

Lathyrus latifolius.

P. J. Redouté. __ 69.

Victor.

Pois de senteur.   *Lathyrus odoratus.*

P. J. Redouté. _ 70.   Langlois.

Nerium.

Laurier Rose.

P. J. Redouté. _ 11.

Langlois.

Lavatera Phoenicea.

Hibiscus.

P. J. Redouté. _ 72.

Bessin.

Lilas.

P. J. Redouté. — 73 .

Langlois .

Liseron.

Convolvulus tricolor.

P. J. Redouté. __ 74 .

Chaptay.

Lychnide a grandes fleurs. *Lychnis grandiflora.*

Le Lis blanc.　　　　　　　　*Lilium candidum.*

Magnolia Soulangiana.

Mauve pourpre.

Malva purpurea.

P. J. Redouté. _ 78 .

Chapuy.

Mimulus.

Muflier a grandes fleurs.   *Antirrhinum.*

P. J. Redouté _ 80.

*Le ne m'oubliez pas
ou Vergissmeinnicht.*

Myosotis scorpioides.

P. J. Redouté. — 81.

Langlois.

Narcisses doubles.　　　　　　　　*Narcissus Gouani.*

P. J. Redouté — 82.　　　　　　　　Bessin.

Narcisse à plusieurs fleurs.　　　　　*Narcissus tazetta.*

P. J. Redouté. _ 83 .

Narcisse à plusieurs fleurs. Var.

P. J. Redouté. _ 84.

Narcissus tazetta. Var.

Chapuy.

Noisetier franc à gros fruits.

Corylus maxima.

P. J. Redouté — 85.

Langlois

Nymphæa Cærulea.

Tagetes.

Œillet d'inde.

P. J. Redouté _ 87.

Bessin.

Œillet panaché.

Dianthus caryophyllus.

P.J. Redouté. _ 88.

Chapuy.

Œillet Variété.

P. J. Redouté. _ 89.

Langlois.

Oranger à fruits déprimés.

P. J. Redouté. — 89 bis

Langlois.

Papaver.

Cambricum.

P.J. Redouté. — 90.

Langlois.

Passiflore ailée.   *Passiflora alata.*

P. J. Redouté ___ 91.   Langlois

Grenadille à grappes.

Passiflora racemosa.

P. J. Redouté _ 92 .

Langlois

Pavot.   *Papaver.*

P. J. Redouté. — 93.   Langlois

La Pêche.

Pêcher à fruits lisses.

P. J. Redouté. __ 95 .   Victor .

La Pensée.

Viola tricolor

Langlois.

Bouquet de Pensées.

Pervenche.

Phalangium.

Lis S.t Bruno.

P. J. Redouté. _ 99.

Victor.

Phlox Reptans.

Pivoine de la Chine.   *Pæonia.*

P. J. Redouté. _101.   Victor.

Pivoine. *Pæonia officinalis.*

P. J. Redouté. _ 102.

Bessin.

Pæonia tenuifolia.

Pivoine à feuilles Linaires.

P. J. Redouté. _ 103 .

Chapuy.

Pivoine odorante.　　　　　*Pæonia flagrans.*

P. J. Redouté . _ 104.　　　　　Langlois.

Pivoine officinale à fleurs simples.   *Pæonia officinalis mas.*

P.J. Redouté. __ 105.   Langlois

Platylobium.

Podalyria Australis.

P. J. Redouté. _107.

Victor.

Poire Tarquin.

P. J. Redouté. __ 108 .

Victor.

Fleurs de Pommier.

Flores Mali.

Oreilles d'Ours.

Primula auricula.

P. J. Redouté. — 110.

Langlois.

Oreilles d'Ours Var.　　　　　Primula Auricula Var.

P. J. Redouté. _ III.　　　　　　　　　Victor.

Primevere.   *Grandiflore.*

P. J. Redouté. _ 112.   Bessin.

Primevere de Chine.   *Primula Sinensis.*

P. J. Redouté. — 113   Bessin.

Prune Royale.

Prunus Domestica.

P. J. Redouté. ─114.

Langlois.

Cornichons blancs.

Var. de Raisins.

Redutea heterophylla.

P. J. Redouté. — 115.

Bessin.

Reine Claude franche.

Rosa Centifolia. *Rosier à cent feuilles.*

P. J. Redouté. _ 117. Langlois.

Rosa centifolia.   *Rosier à cent feuilles.*

P. J. Redouté . 118 .   Langlois .

Rosa centifolia.   *Rosier à cent feuilles.*

Rosa Centifolia Bullata.   *Rosier à feuilles de Laitue.*

P. J. Redouté _ 120.   Langlois.

Rosa Gallica Aurelianensis.　　　*La Duchesse d'Orléans.*

P. J. Redouté. — 121.　　　Langlois.

Rosa Indica.

Rosier des Indes jaune.

P. J. Redouté _ 122.

Bossin.

Bengale Thé hyménée.

P. J. Redouté. _123.

Victor.

Rosa Muscosa.   *Rosier Mousseux.*

P.J.Redouté *124*   *Victor.*

Rose.   *Anémone.*   *Clématite.*

P. J. Redouté. — 125 .   Victor.

Adélaïde d'Orléans.   *Adelia Aurelianensis.*

P. J. Redouté. _ 126.   *Victor.*

Variétés de Rose jaune *et de* Rose du Bengale.   Rosa lutea & Rosa Indica (Var.)

P. J. Redouté. 127.   Langlois.

Rose jaune de soufre.   *Rosa sulfurea.*

P. J. Redouté. _ 128.   Langlois.

Rosier de Bancks var. *à fleurs jaunes.*

Rosier de Candolle Variété.

P. J. Redouté._130.

Langlois.

Rosier à cent-feuilles, foliacé.

Rosa Indica   *Grande Indienne.*

P. J. Redouté. — 132.

Bessin.

Rosier Pompon.   Rosa Pomponia.

P. J. Redouté. _133.   Victor.

Sabot des Alpes.

P. J. Redouté. — 134.

Langlois.

Spaendoncea tamarandifolia.

Gloxinie Var.

Gloxinis Var.

P. J. Redouté. __ 137.

Langlois.

Tigridie queue de Paon.

Tigridia Pavonia.

P. J. Redouté. — 138.

Victor.

Tropæolum majus Var.

Capucine mordorée.

P. J. Redouté. — 139.

Tubereuse.　　　　　　　　　　　　*Tuberosa.*

P. J. Redouté. _140.　　　　　　　　　　Chapuy.

Tulipe de Gesner.   *Tulipa Gesneriana.*

P. J. Redouté. _ 141.   Langlois.

Tulipe cultivée (Variété)

Tulipa culta (Var.)

P. J. Redouté. _ 142.

Langlois.

Tulipier. *Tulipifera.*

Bessin.

(N.º 2.)

(N.º 1.)

(N.º 3.)

(N.º 1.)

Vieußeuxie à taches bleues.

(N.ºs 2. et 3.) *Ixia* (*Variété*)

P. J. Redouté. _ 144

Langlois.